Mobil New Z

Nat

of

G000112624

Mobil New Zealand Nature Series

Native Trees
of New Zealand 2

J. T. Salmon

REED

Front cover: Old nikau palms.
Title page: Upper surface of a mamaku rachis.

Published by Reed Books, a division of Reed Publishing (NZ) Ltd,
39 Rawene Road, Birkenhead, Auckland. Associated companies,
branches and representatives throughout the world.

First published 1998
Text © J. T. Salmon 1998
Photographs © J. T. Salmon 1998
Layout by Graeme Leather

ISBN 0 7900 0559 X

Printed in Singapore

Contents

Introduction

Native Trees of New Zealand 1 and *2* provide concise, portable guides to the identification of New Zealand's native trees. The text and photographs are based on my larger book, *The Trees in New Zealand: Native Trees*, although the number of photographs and species selected is, of course, much reduced. I refer readers to the larger book for a full introduction to New Zealand's forests and native trees.

The classification system used is based on *Flora of New Zealand* (Vol. 1, 1961, by H.H. Allan and Vol. 2, 1970, by L.B. Moore and E. Edgar). Common names and the Maori names for the trees, wherever they exist, are included with the botanical names. Technical terms are kept to a minimum, and those used are explained in the glossary.

Few places in New Zealand are far from 'the bush': our forest parks and national parks preserve large tracts, often in something close to their original state; forest remnants are found in many smaller reserves, on farmland, alongside rivers and streams, and around the coastline; many species are cultivated in parks and gardens. These books aim to provide easy identification of the major species likely to be found by the bush walker or botanical enthusiast. I hope they contribute to readers' enjoyment and appreciation of our distinctive native trees.

J. T. Salmon

Silver beech / Tawhai
Nothofagus menziesii

Appearance

- Tall tree with tiered branches; in open broad, spreading and dome-shaped with lower branches arching towards ground; often dwarfed in mountains above bush line.
- *Height:* up to 30 m.
- *Trunk:* up to 2 m through; often buttressed.
- *Bark:* silvery-white on young trees; grey, flaky on old trees.

Foliage, Flowers & Fruit

- *Foliage:* thick, leathery, rigid leaves are mid-green and gland-dotted above, new leaves often yellowish with orange-red margins, principal veins not very distinct below, domatia (pits) visible; 6–15 mm long, 5–15 mm wide, on petioles up to 3 mm long; alternately arranged; doubly crenate (shallow, rounded teeth). Branchlets, petioles and peduncles clothed with brownish hairs.
- *Flowers:* Nov–Jan; orange-red; sexes together on same tree; male inflorescences arise on stalks from branchlets, 1–4 per stalk, each consist of a single flower on sparsely hairy peduncle about 3 mm long; female 1–4 per stalk, arising between the leaf axils, further towards tip of branchlet, each 2–3 flowered.
- *Fruit:* ripens Jan; nut inside

4-segmented cupule covered by 4–5 rows of processes with swollen glands at tips.

Distribution & Habitat

- From Thames south in forests; some dwarf trees above bush line in mountains.
- Sea level to 900 m.

▼ Gland-dotted upper sides of two leaves. (x3)

▼ Undersurface of leaf showing vein pattern, thick edges, and two domatia. (x3)

◀ Female flower, Jan. (x2)

2 Hard beech / Tawhairaunui
Nothofagus truncata

Appearance
- Tall tree with tiered branches; in open broad, spreading and dome-shaped with lower branches arching towards ground; often dwarfed in mountains above bush line; partly deciduous in late winter.

- *Height:* up to 30 m.
- *Trunk:* up to 2 m through; often buttressed.
- *Bark:* silvery-white on young trees; grey, flaky on old trees.

Foliage, Flowers & Fruit

- *Foliage:* young leaves lighter green than older leaves, mature leaves glossy dark-green above, yellow-green and paler below; 25–35 mm long, 20 mm wide, on petioles 2–3 mm long; broadly ovate to elliptic-oblong or rounded in shape, margins coarsely and bluntly serrate; hairless except when young.

- *Flowers:* Nov–Jan; red or orange forms; male inflorescences occur 1–10 per branchlet, each with 1–3 subsessile flowers of 10–13 stamens, anthers 3 mm long; female inflorescences arising 1–5 per branchlet are sessile, 2–3 mm long, ovoid, 3-flowered.

- *Fruit:* ripens Jan; nut inside 4-segmented cupule covered by 4–5 rows of processes with swollen glands at tips.

Distribution & Habitat

- From Mangonui south to Greymouth and Wairau River in Marlborough.
- Sea level to 900 m.

▼ Male flowers and truncated leaves. ▼ Lower leaf surfaces. (approx x1)

3 Red beech / Tawhairaunui
Nothofagus fusca

Appearance
- Very tall tree with spreading to ascending branches.
- *Height:* up to 30 m.
- *Trunk:* up to 2–3 m through; very straight; often buttressed.
- *Bark:* juvenile smooth, whitish; old trees grey, deeply furrowed.

Foliage, Flowers & Fruit
- *Foliage:* thin, leathery leaves are bright pale green above, duller below with domatia (pits) in axils of lower lateral veins; venation distinct on both surfaces; 2–4 cm long, 1.5–2.5 cm wide; alternately arranged; broadly ovate or ovate-

oblong in shape with deeply cut margins and prominent teeth which distinguish it from the hard beech. Juvenile foliage deep bright red colour during winter. Mature trees drop leaves as new leaves open during spring.

- *Flowers:* irregular intervals; profusion of red colour; male inflorescences arise 1–8 per branchlet, each on 4 mm long peduncle, consisting of 1–3 flowers; female inflorescence is axillary, sessile, ovoid, 3-flowered.
- *Fruit:* ripens Jan; 3-angled or flat nut, about 7 mm long, slightly reddish on margins.

Distribution & Habitat
- From Te Aroha south to Fiordland in lowland and mountain forests.
- Sea level to 1050 m.

▲ Typical, alternate leaves, upper surfaces. (approx x1)

▶ Male inflorescences, Nov.

Black beech / Tawhairauriki
Nothofagus solandri

Appearance

- Medium-sized forest tree, with branches spreading in tiers and forming a broad crown.
- *Height:* to 25 m.
- *Trunk:* up to 1 m through.
- *Bark:* juvenile pale, smooth and faintly furrowed; old trees dark, furrowed, flaky, often covered in thick, black, velvety fungus.

Foliage, Flowers & Fruit

- *Foliage:* leaves are glossy dark-green above, pale with greyish-white hairs below; 10–15 mm long, 5–10 mm wide, on petioles 1–2 mm long; alternately arranged; narrow-oblong to elliptic-oblong in shape with rolled-down edges and rounded tips. Branchlets, leaf petioles have short golden hairs.

- *Flowers:* Oct–Dec; male inflorescences arise 1–4 per stalk with 1 or 2 flowers, each with 6–17 bright-red stamens arising from brownish-green, bell-shaped perianths; female inflorescences are tiny, 1–3 flowered, arise in leaf axils beyond the male inflorescences. More profuse than other beeches.

- *Fruit:* ripens Nov after 12 months; 2 or 3-seeded cupule.

Distribution & Habitat

- Throughout North and South Is. in lowland and mountain forest south of a line joining southern Waikato and East Cape.
- Sea level to 750 m.

▼ Spray of black beech. (x1.5)

▼ Male flowers of a black beech, Oct.

◀ Grove of black beech trees.

Ongaonga / Tree nettle
Urtica ferox

Appearance

- Shrub or small, soft-wooded tree with many, often intertwining, branches.
- *Height:* up to 3 m.

- *Trunk:* up to 12 cm through.
- *Bark:* dark coloured and bearing spines.

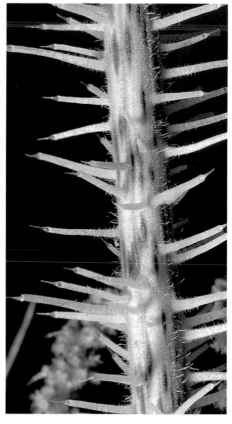

▲ A branchlet showing the large spines that identify this plant which grows as a low sprawling shrub or a small tree with intertwining and tangled branches (x3.5).

Foliage, Flowers & Fruit

- *Foliage:* thin, membraneous leaves are pale green above, the prominent midvein with stinging hairs, slightly paler below with soft hairs; 8–12 cm long (juvenile up to 15 cm), 3–5 cm wide, on petioles up to 5 cm long; oppositely arranged; ovate-triangular in shape with a truncate or semicordate base, tips pointed, marginal teeth up to 1 cm long with rows of stinging hairs. Branches, branchlets, petioles and flower spikes also bear stinging hairs.

- *Flowers:* Dec; tiny greenish white flowers arise from leaf axils on spikes up to 8 cm long; sexes on different trees.

- *Fruit:* ripens Jan; brown, ovoid seed about 1.5 mm long.

Distribution & Habitat

- Throughout North Is. and along west coast of South Is. in scrubland and along forest margins.

- Sea level to 600 m.

▼ Female flower spikes. (x0.25)

▼ Leaf upper surface, with male flowers arising in the leaf axil. (x0.75)

6 Karaka
Corynocarpus laevigatus

Appearance
- Leafy broad canopy tree with stout, spreading branches in forest; in open may develop a secondary layer of branches.

- *Height:* up to 15 m.
- *Trunk:* up to 60 cm through.
- *Bark:* grey-brown; smooth.

Foliage, Flowers & Fruit

- *Foliage:* thick, leathery leaves are glossy green above, slightly paler below with prominent midvein; 10–15 cm, sometimes 20 cm long, 5–7 cm wide, on stout petioles 10–15 mm long; elliptic to obovate-oblong in shape, margins recurved (bend backwards).
- *Flowers:* Oct; bisexual; greenish-white flowers 4–5 mm in diameter arise on stiff, stout terminal panicles up to 20 cm long.

- *Fruit:* ripens Feb; large numbers of distinctive, orange, heavy, fleshy drupes 2.5–4 cm long hang downwards; unpleasant smell from fallen, rotting fruits.

Distribution & Habitat

- Coastal regions throughout North, South and Chatham Is. (less common in South Is.) and at the Kermadecs; often in groves.

▼ Leaf upper surface. (x0.5)

▼ Karaka drupes, Feb. (approx x1)

7 Kaikomako
Pennantia corymbosa

Appearance

- Slender canopy tree; juvenile stage may last for many years: straggling, twiggy plant with interlacing branches carrying sparse leaves.

- *Height:* up to 12 m.
- *Trunk:* up to 20 cm through.
- *Bark:* grey-white; smooth.

Foliage, Flowers & Fruit

- *Foliage:* leaves of juveniles 7–15 mm long, 5–10 mm wide on petioles 2–3 mm long; obovate, cuneate at base and lobed or toothed around apex; occur far apart on branches. The thick, leathery adult leaves are dark green above, paler below; 5–10 cm long, 1–4 cm wide on petioles 1 cm long; alternate to sub-opposite; oblong to obovate-oblong in shape, coarsely crenate-dentate or lobed. Leaf petioles, branchlets and inflorescences hairy.

- *Flowers:* Dec; profuse creamy-white fragrant flowers on 4–8 cm long panicles; male, female and sometimes bisexual flowers on separate trees.

- *Fruit:* ripens Mar; shining black, ovoid drupe; the favourite food of the bellbird (korimako), for which the tree takes its name.

Distribution & Habitat

- Throughout North and South Is. in lowland forests.
- Sea level to 600 m.

▼ Spray of leaves and drupes, Mar.

▼ A juvenile kaikomako.

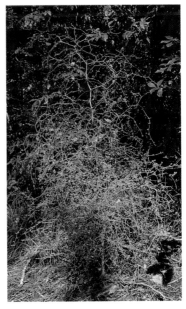

Matagouri / Wild Irishman
Discaria toumatou

Appearance

- Branching, thorny shrub or small tree with spreading branches.
- *Height:* up to 6 m.
- *Trunk:* up to 20 cm through.
- *Bark:* grey; rough, chunky.

Foliage, Flowers & Fruit

- *Foliage:* thick, leathery leaves are glossy mid-green above, paler below; 5–20 mm long, 2–5 mm wide; arise either singly, in bundles from below thorn axils, or opposite

on short shoots; narrow-obovate to obovate-oblong in shape. Deciduous in high country.

- *Flowers:* Oct; white; 3–5 mm across, arise singly or in fascicles on short, hairy pedicels from below axils of thorns.
- *Fruit:* ripens Apr; red, globose, 3-lobed fruit about 5 mm across.

Distribution & Habitat

- Abundant along east of South Is., sparse along west of North and South Is; in open tussock, dune country and rocky places.
- Sea level to 900 m.

▼ Branchlet showing fascicles of flowers and leaves, Oct.

▼ Matagouri in full flower. Stiff, hard thorns arise along the branchlets.

▶ The rough, chunky bark.

9 Kohekohe
Dysoxylum spectabile

Appearance

- Canopy tree with stout, spreading branches.
- *Height:* up to 15 m.
- *Trunk:* columnar; up to 1 m through.
- *Bark:* reddish-brown; smooth; often lichen-covered.

Foliage, Flowers & Fruit

- *Foliage:* leaves glossy green above, paler yellow-green below; pinnately compound with petioles about 4 cm long; opposite or subopposite leaflets have petiolules about 1.5 cm long; undulate, slightly leathery leaf blades, ovate to obovate oblong.

- *Flowers:* May–Aug; long drooping clusters of panicles of greenish-white waxy flowers sprout from trunk and branches; inflorescences up to 30 cm long, flowers with quite thick petals are up to 3 cm across on short pedicels. Individual trees flower in alternate years.
- *Fruit:* ripens following May; fleshy 3–4-celled seed capsules up to 2.5 cm across, several to a stalk; red arils hold 2 seeds in each cell.

Distribution & Habitat

- From North Cape south to Nelson in damp situations in coastal forests.
- Sea level to 100 m.

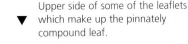

▼ An individual flower showing the thick, waxy petals and greenish sepals, Aug. (x2)

▼ Upper side of some of the leaflets which make up the pinnately compound leaf.

◀ Mature seed capsules, May. (x1)

Titoki
Alectryon excelsus

Appearance

- Tree with short trunk, and wide-spreading branches.
- *Height:* up to 10 m.
- *Trunk:* up to 60 cm through; short, stout.
- *Bark:* grey; smooth; often lichen-covered.

Foliage, Flowers & Fruit

- *Foliage:* leaves shiny mid-green above, paler below; young leaves paler; 10–40 cm long on petioles about 8 cm long; imparipinnate; each leaf consists of 4–6 pairs of alternate to subopposite leaflets with petiolules about 5 mm long.

Leaflets 5–10 cm long by 2–5 cm wide; ovate-oblong to ovate-lanceolate, sinnuate, with margins serrate, dentate or simple. Branchlets and petioles hairy.

- *Flowers:* Nov; unisexual; densely hairy, purple, fragrant flowers in axillary panicles up to 30 cm long; each flower 3–4 mm in diameter with 5 basally fused hairy sepals, no petals.
- *Fruit:* ripens Dec after 12 months; somewhat woody seed capsules with brownish hairy clothing; glossy black seed partly embedded in scarlet, fleshy aril.

Distribution & Habitat

- From North Cape to Banks Peninsula in the east and to about Bruce Bay in the west, in lowland forests, particularly river flats.
- Sea level to 600 m.

▼ Leaf upper surface.

▼ Panicle of seed capsules, Dec. (x1)

Akeake
Dodonaea viscosa

Appearance

- A hardy, erect shrub or small tree with spreading, gently ascending branches.
- *Height:* up to 7 m.
- *Trunk:* up to 20 cm through.
- *Bark:* reddish, peels in thick flakes.

Foliage, Flowers & Fruit

- *Foliage:* leaves mid-green above, only slightly paler below with prominent midvein; 4–10 cm long, 1–3 cm wide, gradually narrowing to a petiole about 1 cm long; alternate to subopposite; narrow-

obovate to narrow-elliptic in shape, with blunt tips. Branchlets sticky.

- *Flowers:* Oct; yellow; without petals, arise in terminal, densely flowered panicles up to 4 cm long; each flower on pubescent pedicel 4 mm long; predominantly unisexual on the common form, the coloured form 'Purpurea' bears many bisexual flowers.
- *Fruit:* ripens Dec; yellowish-red, compressed seed capsule about 15 mm across with 2–3 thin, veined, broad, lobed wings. *Purpurea* form: bright purplish-red capsules.

Distribution & Habitat

- From North Cape south to Banks Peninsula and about Greymouth in coastal and lowland shrub and forests. Also on the Chatham Is. The form 'Purpurea' is widely cultivated in parks and gardens.
- Sea level to 550 m.

▼ Leaf upper surface. (approx x1)

▼ Typical flower panicle, Oct.

Pate
Schefflera digitata

Appearance

- Small, spreading, low-growing tree with stout branches.
- *Height:* up to 8 m.
- *Trunk:* up to 15 cm through.
- *Bark:* greenish; smooth.

Foliage, Flowers & Fruit

- *Foliage:* large compound leaves on long, stout petioles up to 25 cm long; 3–9 thin, soft leaflets are glossy green above, paler below with prominent midveins, on reddish petiolules up to 2 cm long; obovate-cuneate in shape, with sharply serrate margins. In the North Is. a juvenile stage occurs in which leaves are irregularly lobed or pinnatifid.

- *Flowers:* Feb; a large drooping inflorescence up to 35 cm across arises towards end of branches, just below or among the leaves, formed of umbels of up to 10 small (7 mm wide), greenish flowers arising irregularly along branches of a panicle.

- *Fruit:* ripens Apr–May; large, spectacular clusters of purple-black fruits, fleshy, roundish, about 3.5 mm across.

Distribution & Habitat

- North, South and Stewart Is. in damp parts of forests, along stream banks or shady roadsides through bush.
- Sea level to 1200 m.

▲ LEFT: Branch showing leaf undersides and long, stout petioles of the compound leaves.

▲ RIGHT: Central leaflet of the compound leaf. (approx x1)

▶ An inflorescence, Feb.

Five-finger / Whauwhaupaku / Puahou
Pseudopanax arboreus

Appearance

- Small, much branched, round-headed tree with thick, brittle, spreading branches; can be epiphytic on tree fern trunks with roots descending to ground.
- *Height:* up to 8 m.
- *Trunk:* up to 25 cm through.
- *Bark:* adult rough, corky; juvenile relatively smooth, dark streaks, shows transverse leaf scars.

Foliage, Flowers & Fruit

- *Foliage:* rather thick, leathery, compound leaves, glossy green above and paler below, on petioles 15–20 cm long; 5–7 leaflets 10–20 cm long by 4–7 cm wide, on petiolules 1–3.5 cm long; obovate-oblong to oblong-cuneate in shape, with coarsely serrate or dentate margins.
- *Flowers:* Jun–Sept; profuse sweet-

scented, yellowish-white flowers
(which darken after pollination)
occur in terminal compound
umbels, with 10–15 flowers per
umbellule. Males 7–8 mm across;
females about 3 mm across.

- *Fruit:* ripens Sept; purplish-black,
  5–8 mm across.

Distribution & Habitat

- From North Cape to Southland in
  forests and open scrub; one of the
  most common native trees.
- Sea level to 760 m.

▼ Male flowers and buds
   smothering the foliage, Aug.

▼ Typical leaf. (x0.3)

◀ A mature tree with flowers, Sept.

Appearance

- Passes through different juvenile stages, the longest 15–20 years when leaves are rigid, narrow and up to 1 m long, surrounding the top of the 4.5–6 m stem like the ribs of a partially opened umbrella. The stem then branches at the top to begin the adult stage of a round-headed tree.

- *Height:* up to 15 m.
- *Trunk:* straight; up to 50 cm through.
- *Bark:* varies from brown to grey; often lichen-covered.

Foliage, Flowers & Fruit

- *Foliage:* adult leaves are thick, leathery and upright, dark green above and paler below; 10–20 cm long, 2–3 cm wide; margins are toothed.
- *Flowers:* Feb; creamy-green flowers occur in irregular compound terminal umbels forming large clusters; petals fold out as flower opens.

- *Fruit:* ripens Mar; ovoid, purplish subglobose fruits 4–5 mm wide.

Distribution & Habitat

- North, South and Stewart Is. in forest and scrubland.
- Sea level to 760 m.

▲ The umbrella-like form of a young tree.

▼ Lancewood fruits, March.

▲ Upper surface of adult leaves. (x0.6)

◄ Juvenile forms at left and right foreground, with an adult tree in centre and a juvenile changing to adult.

15 Papauma / Broadleaf
Griselinia littoralis

Appearance

- In the open forms a tight, bushy tree; in the forest it is more open.
- *Height:* to 15 m.
- *Trunk:* up to 24 cm through.
- *Bark:* reddish brown; blistery and furrowed.

Foliage, Flowers & Fruit

- *Foliage:* thick leaves are shiny yellow-green above with distinct venation, duller below with obscure venation; 5–10 cm long by 2–5 cm wide; broad-ovate to ovate-oblong in shape, with a rounded tip, usually equal-sided at the base, on stout petioles 1–2 cm long.
- *Flowers:* Apr; greenish-petalled flowers occur in panicles from leaf axils towards branchlet tips,

▼ A papauma tree.

sometimes only simple racemes; each flower 4–6 mm diameter; unisexual on separate trees.

- *Fruit:* ripens Mar; green, ovoid, 6–7 mm long.

Distribution & Habitat

- From Mangonui south to Stewart Is. in forest.
- Sea level to 900 m.

◀ Papauma leaves, upper surface. (approx x0.70)

◀ Papauma flower panicles, April.

16 Mingimingi
Leucopogon fasciculatus

Appearance

- A shrub or small tree; openly branched.
- *Height:* up to 6 m.
- *Trunk:* up to 10 cm through.
- *Bark:* brownish-grey; flaky, peels off in thin strips.

Foliage, Flowers & Fruit

- *Foliage:* leaves are mid-green above, slightly paler below; 12–25 mm long, 2–4 mm wide; narrow-lanceolate or linear-oblong in shape, spreading and sharp pointed, with finely serrated hairy

margins. Branchlets are hairy.

- *Flowers:* Oct; sweetly fragrant, pale green-white flowers, 3–4 mm long, occur in axillary or terminal drooping racemes of 6–12 flowers each. Petals and stalks hairy.

- *Fruit:* ripens Apr; berries are red or sometimes white, oblong, 2–4 mm long.

Distribution & Habitat

- From Three Kings Is. and North Cape south to Canterbury in coastal or lowland scrub or forest, and in rocky places.

- Sea level to 1150 m.

▲ LEFT: Upper and lower leaf surfaces. Branchlets are pubescent.

▲ RIGHT: A drooping raceme of flowers, Oct. (x2)

▶ Ripening fruits, Apr. (x3.5)

Mountain neinei
Dracophyllum traversii

Appearance

- Stoutly branching tree with candelabra-like branches and tufts of foliage.

- *Height:* up to 13 m.
- *Trunk:* up to 60 cm through.
- *Bark:* greyish; peeling.

Foliage, Flowers & Fruit

- *Foliage:* leaf blades are glossy mid-green above and below; 30–60 cm long, 4–5 cm wide, with a sheath 3 cm long; smooth margins; red-brown fallen leaves persist on forest floor for long time.
- *Flowers:* Nov–Dec; small red flowers crowded on a densely branched, terminal panicle.
- *Fruit:* ripens Jan; panicles of round, purplish seed capsules about 2.5 mm across.

Distribution & Habitat

- In montane and subalpine regions from Nelson to about Arthur's Pass, in forest and scrub.
- 760–1400 m.

▼ Immature seed head, Jan.

▼ Typical peeling bark.

Inanga
Dracophyllum longifolium

Appearance

- Tree with slender, erect or spreading branches and branchlets.
- *Height:* up to 12 m.
- *Trunk:* up to 10 cm through.

Foliage, Flowers & Fruit

- *Foliage:* rigid, leathery leaf blades are light green above and below, tips brown; usually crowded towards tips of branchlets; blades

▼ Leaf tuft.

10–25 cm long, 2–4 mm wide; tapering to long acuminate tip, margins smooth and sometimes minutely serrate; ciliated (fringed with hairs on margin) shoulder on sheath.

- *Flowers:* Dec; white flowers on drooping 6–15-flowered racemes up to 5 cm long, occur terminally on short lateral branches.
- *Fruit:* ripens Jan–Feb.

Distribution & Habitat

- Most widespread of *Dacrophyllum* genus. Found in coastal, lowland and subalpine scrub and forest from East Cape south in North, South and Stewart Is. and the Auckland and Chatham Is.
- Sea level to 600 m.

▼ Leaf shoulder. (x5)

▼ Flower racemes, Dec. (x0.3)

Tawapou
Poutiera costata

Appearance

- Small, closely-branched tree; gnarled and ragged in exposed places.
- *Height:* up to 15 m.
- *Trunk:* up to 1 m through.
- *Bark:* grey to brownish-grey; rough.

Foliage, Flowers & Fruit

- *Foliage:* thick, leathery leaves are glossy dark green above with prominent venation, slightly paler below with raised midvein; 5–10 cm long, 2–5 cm wide; alternately arranged; elliptic to obovate-oblong in shape, with blunt tips and cuneately narrowed at the base. Branchlets, petioles clothed

▼ Glossy mature leaves and young foliage clad in short soft hairs.

with appressed hairs, bleed milky latex when cut.

- *Flowers:* Jan; greenish-cream; 4–6 mm in diameter; generally bisexual but sometimes unisexual, arise singly, occasionally in pairs, on stout peduncles about 12 mm long mostly from leaf axils but also directly from branches.
- *Fruit:* ripens Feb–Apr after 12–15 months; ovoid berry up to 2.5 cm long, changing from green to deep red; contains up to 4 hard, smooth seeds almost as long as the berry.

Distribution & Habitat

- From North Cape south to Tolaga Bay in east and Manukau Harbour in west sporadically on islands and headlands, always close to the sea.
- Sea level to 450 m.

▼ Tawapou tree.

▼ Spray showing axillary flowers, Jan.

► The distinctive berries at various stages of ripening.

Mapou / Mapau / Red matipo
Myrsine australis

Appearance

- Shrub or small tree.
- *Height:* up to 6 m.
- *Trunk:* up to 60 cm through.
- *Bark:* grey or dark brown; smooth.

Foliage, Flowers & Fruit

- *Foliage:* smooth, leathery leaves are pale green above, often with reddish spots, and with a hairy midvein, pale green below; 3–6 cm

long, 1.5–2.5 cm wide, on red petioles up to 5 mm long; obovate-oblong to broadly elliptic in shape, with usually strongly undulate margins. Branchlets and young branches reddish.

- *Flowers:* Dec–Jan; unisexual; creamy-yellow flowers up to 2.5 mm across on short pedicels arise in crowded clusters along bare branches, usually below leaves; smaller female flowers have a large, fringed stigma.

- *Fruit:* ripens Apr; black, ovoid drupes about 3 mm wide, clustered around branchlets.

Distribution & Habitat
- Throughout North, South and Stewart Is. along forest margins, in scrublands and sometimes inside forests.
- Sea level to 900 m.

▼ Mature drupes cluster around a branchlet.

▼ Leaf midveins are hairy; branchlets and petioles are red.

21 Toro
Myrsine salicina

Appearance
- Small, open-branched tree.
- *Height:* up to 8 m.
- *Trunk:* up to 25 cm through.
- *Bark:* black or dark red-brown as ages; thick, furrowed.

Foliage, Flowers & Fruit
- *Foliage:* leathery, smooth leaves are mid-green above with distinct midvein, paler below; elongated oil tubes resemble veins; 7–18 cm long, 2–3 cm wide; alternately arranged; narrow-elliptic to narrow-oblong in shape, with rounded tip and gradually narrowing base. New shoots are yellow-green, young branchlets reddish.
- *Flowers:* Nov; bisexual; long, dense

clusters of pinkish white flowers about 3 mm in diameter arise along branchlets below leaves.

- *Fruit:* ripens Dec; red, ovoid drupes up to 9 mm long.

Distribution & Habitat

- In forests from North Cape to about Greymouth; more common in the North Is., absent in the east of the South Is.
- Sea level to 850 m.

▲ LEFT: Upper surfaces of leaves and terminal shoot.

▲ RIGHT: Young shoots are yellowish green; branchlets are reddish-tinged.

▶ Toro drupes; the red ones are ripe, Dec. (x0.5)

◀ Crown of toro in flower, Nov.

Hangehange
Geniostoma rupestre var. *ligustrifolium*

Appearance

- Bushy, much-branching shrub or small tree; branches quite brittle.
- *Height:* up to 4 m.
- *Trunk:* up to 10–15 cm through.
- *Bark:* brown; rather rough, often clothed with mosses, lichens.

Foliage, Flowers & Fruit

- *Foliage:* leaves are glossy pale green above with indistinct venation, paler and duller below with prominent raised veins; 5–7 cm long, 2–3 cm wide, on slender petioles 5–10 mm long; oppositely

arranged; obovate to broad or elliptic-ovate in shape, abruptly narrowing to an acuminate tip.

- *Flowers:* Oct; unisexual with male and female on separate plants; inflorescences of faintly lemon-scented, hairy, greenish-white to white flowers, 6 mm across.
- *Fruit:* ripens Mar; green turning black capsules 5–7 mm long, 5 mm in diameter, on drooping stalks around branchlets.

Distribution & Habitat

- Abundant among larger trees in coastal and lowland forest from Three Kings Is. south to Golden Bay and Marlborough Sounds.
- Sea level to 100 m.

▲ Left: Flowers, Oct. (x2)

▲ Right: Upper surfaces of leaves.

▶ Leaf undersides.

◀ A small tree growing in the forest.

Black maire / Maire
Nestegis cunninghamii

Appearance

- Tall, canopy tree with large crown.
- *Height:* up to 20 m.
- *Trunk:* up to 1.5 m through; straight.
- *Bark:* brown; rough, corky.

Foliage, Flowers & Fruit

- *Foliage:* leathery leaves are dark green above, paler below with prominent midveins; leaves of juvenile 15–25 cm long, 8–16 cm wide; oppositely arranged; narrow-linear in shape with acute tips; adult leaves 7.5–15 cm long, 1.5–4.5 cm wide, on stout petioles about 10 mm long; lanceolate to obovate-lanceolate with rounded or sub-acute tips.
- *Flowers:* Sept; bisexual or unisexual;

inflorescence of minute, yellow green flowers in an 8–12-flowered raceme, 1–2.5 cm long, arising from leaf axil; raceme axis and flower pedicels densely hairy; borne in great abundance.

- *Fruit:* ripens Oct after 12 months; red or sometimes yellow, ovoid drupes borne in great profusion along branchlets.

Distribution & Habitat

- In isolated forests in North Is., Marlborough and Nelson.
- Sea level to 760 m.

▼ Leaf upper and lower surfaces.

▼ Male flower, Sept. (x4)

▶ Ripe drupes, with next season's drupes forming in racemes above, Oct. (x0.5)

24 Coastal maire
Nestegis apetala

Appearance

- Small tree, sometimes a shrub, with spreading and often tortuous branches.
- *Height:* up to 6 m.
- *Trunk:* up to 15 cm through.
- *Bark:* brown; rough, furrowed, flaky.

Foliage, Flowers & Fruit

- *Foliage:* leathery leaves are glossy dark green above, pale and duller below, with prominent raised midveins on both surfaces; oppositely arranged; leaves of juvenile up to 14 cm long, 8.5 cm wide, adult 4.5–12.5 cm long by

1.5–6 cm wide, on petioles about 10 mm long; elliptic to broadly elliptic in shape, with often wavy margins.

- *Flowers:* Jan; racemes of up to 21 flowers each arise from leaf axils or directly from branchlets. Individual greenish flowers (unisexual or bisexual) are about 2.5 mm across; no petals.
- *Fruit:* ripens following Dec–Jan; richly purple drupes spotted with white, 9 mm long.

Distribution & Habitat

- On rocky headlands around Whangarei Heads, on the Hen and Chickens, Great and Little Barrier, Fanal, Cuvier and Poor Knights Is. and around the Bay of Islands.
- Sea level to 10–15 m.

▼ Racemes of female flowers, Jan. (x1)

▼ Spray showing leaf upper sides. (x1)

◀ Drupes, December. (x1.5)

25 Karamu
Coprosma lucida

Appearance
- Small tree or shrub with stout, spreading branches.
- *Height:* 3–6 m.
- *Trunk:* up to 15–20 cm through.
- *Bark:* pale brown; finely furrowed, with scattered pustules.

Foliage, Flowers & Fruit
- *Foliage:* leathery leaves are glossy dark green above with a raised midvein, pale below with distinct domatia (pits); 12–19 cm long, 3–4 cm wide, on stout petioles 10–30 mm long.

▼ Foliage spray showing male flower clusters and buds.

- *Flowers:* Oct; female flowers greenish-yellow, male creamy; female more profuse, borne on a 3-branched inflorescence, 3–4 flowers at end of each branch; males have long, delicate filaments, and anthers split lengthwise.
- *Fruit:* ripens Apr after 18 months; clusters of orange-red, oblong drupes 8–12 mm long.

Distribution & Habitat
- Throughout North, South and Stewart Is. in forest, along forest margins and in scrub.
- Sea level to 1060 m.

▼ Drupes, April. (approx x1)

▼ Male flowers. (x1)

▶ Female flowers. (x1)

26

Taupata
Coprosma repens

Appearance

- Hardy shrub or small tree; can grow out of rock crevices; may be gnarled, twisted or prostrate in exposed coastal situations.
- *Height:* to 8 m.
- *Trunk:* slender; up to 10 cm through.
- *Bark:* smooth; pale or greyish-brown.

Foliage, Flowers & Fruit

- *Foliage:* thick, fleshy leaves are glossy dark green above with a prominent midvein and distinct venation, paler below with distinct venation and domatia (pits); 2–3 or 6–8 cm long, 1.5–2 or 4–5 cm wide (the larger leaves occur in shade), on petioles 8–16 mm long; broad-oblong to broadly ovate-

oblong in shape, with rounded to truncate tips and wavy, recurved or inrolled margins.

- *Flowers:* Sept; greenish-white, to 9 mm long, in dense clusters.
- *Fruit:* ripens May–Jun; orange-red, transparent, ovoid drupes borne in profusion.

Distribution & Habitat

- From North Cape to Marlborough and Greymouth in coastal areas.
- Sea level to 500 m.

▼ Taupata leaf upper side. (x1)

▼ Taupata drupes smother the branches.

27

Hakeke / Hakekeke
Olearia ilicifolia

Appearance

- Shrub or small tree with stout branchlets.
- *Height:* up to 5 m.
- *Trunk:* up to 12 cm through.
- *Bark:* brown; thin, papery, peeling in long, thin, narrow strips.

Foliage, Flowers & Fruit

- *Foliage:* stiff, leathery leaves are glossy dark green above with prominent midvein, pale and duller below with satiny, yellowish-white or ochraceous tomentum and prominent midvein; 5–10 cm long, 1–2 cm wide on deeply

grooved petioles 2 cm long; alternately arranged; lanceolate to linear-oblong in shape (broad in South and Stewart Is., narrow in North Is. plants), with sharply dentate-serrate wavy margins (marginal teeth are almost spines), pointed tips and truncate bases. Branchlets hairy. Musky scent.

- *Flowers:* Dec; corymbs of flower heads on long, stout stalks; each head about 8 mm across with 10–15 white florets.
- *Fruit:* ripens Jan–Feb.

Distribution & Habitat

- From East Cape southwards to Stewart Is. mainly in the mountains.
- Sea level to 1200 m.

▲ Upper surface of typical hakeke leaf from North Is. (approx x1)

▲ Lower surface of hakeke leaves have a yellowish-white to ochraceous, satiny tomentum.

28 Heketara
Olearia rani

Appearance
- Spreading tree in open; when enclosed in forest or scrub grows as a shrub or a tree with a slender trunk reaching to light where crown forms.

- *Height:* up to 7.5 m or 2–3 m as shrub.
- *Trunk:* up to 30 cm through.
- *Bark:* brown; thin, furrowed, peeling in narrow flakes.

▼ Tree in full flower, Oct.

Foliage, Flowers & Fruit

- *Foliage:* thin, leathery leaves are glossy dark green above, pale and dull below with prominent raised mid and lateral veins; 5–15 cm long, 5–6.5 cm wide on petioles up to 4 cm long; mainly alternate arrangement; broad elliptic-ovate to oblong in shape, with irregularly or coarsely toothed margins. Branchlets, petioles, leaf undersides and flower branchlets all densely covered with soft, white or pale-fawn tomentum.
- *Flowers:* Sept–Oct; masses of scented white flowers with yellow centres, about 1 cm across, arise on large, long, much-branched panicles, up to 24 florets per head.
- *Fruit:* ripens Mar; small, hard, dry, single-seeded fruit, plumed.

Distribution & Habitat

- One of commonest olearias througout the North Is., growing also in Nelson and Marlborough in forest clearings, along forest margins, streams or river banks and in scrub.
- Sea level to 800 m.

▼ Panicles of flower heads, Nov.

▼ Leaf upper surface.

Streamside tree daisy
Olearia cheesmanii

Appearance

- Erect, much-branching shrub or small tree.
- *Height:* up to 4 m.
- *Trunk:* up to 15 cm through.
- *Bark:* brown; rough, furrowed, continually flaking off in thin strips.

Foliage, Flowers & Fruit

- *Foliage:* leaves are glossy dark green above, pale and dull below with pale, buff-coloured, closely appressed tomentum, prominent midvein and distinct lateral veins; 5–9 cm long, 2–3 cm wide, on winged petioles 2 cm long; linear

▼ Streamside tree daisy in full flower, Oct.

to narrow-lanceolate or oblong-lanceolate in shape. Branchlets are grooved and tomentose.

- *Flowers:* Sept–Oct; white with yellow centres; the tree smothered in corymbs up to 15 cm across; each flower head about 1.5 cm across.
- *Fruit:* ripens Mar; small, hard, dry single-seeded fruit.

Distribution & Habitat

- From Coromandel Peninsula south to about Westport, mainly west of the main divide, along streamsides near forest margins.
- Sea level to 1000 m.

▲ LEFT: Leaf underside. (x1)

▲ RIGHT: The grooved, tomentose branchlet and a petiole. (x2)

▶ The rough and furrowed bark.

30 Rough-leaved tree daisy
Olearia lacunosa

Appearance
- Shrub or small tree with thick, twisted, sometimes gnarled branches.
- *Height:* up to 5 m.
- *Trunk:* up to 25 cm through.
- *Bark:* brown; thin, papery, peels in long, narrow flakes; several layers thick.

Foliage, Flowers & Fruit
- *Foliage:* very thick, leathery leaves are dark green and wrinkled above with midvein very prominent, lateral veins almost at right angles to it, lower surface duller and pitted; 7.5–17 cm long, 8 mm–2.5 cm wide; linear to linear-oblong in shape, with acute or acuminate

▼ Rough-leaved tree daisies.

tips. Branchlets, petioles, leaf lower surfaces and flower cluster stalks all clothed with dense brown to reddish-brown tomentum.

- *Flowers:* Jan; corymbs on long stalks around branchlet end; flower head about 1 cm across, 8–12 white florets.
- *Fruit:* ripens Mar; small, hard, dry, single-seeded fruit.

Distribution & Habitat

- From Tararua Range south to about Franz Josef Glacier in mountain forests and scrub.
- 600–900 m.

◄ A spray of foliage showing upper and lower leaf surfaces.

◄ Corymbs of flower heads on long stalks around the end of a branchlet, Jan.

31

Rangiora
Brachyglottis repanda

Appearance

- A spreading shrub or small bushy tree with stout, brittle, spreading branches.
- *Height:* up to 7 m.
- *Bark:* greyish-brown; smooth.

Foliage, Flowers & Fruit

- *Foliage:* somewhat leathery, membraneous leaves are dull or slightly shining above, white with closely appressed tomentum below and prominent raised veins;

5–25 cm long, 5–20 cm wide, on stout, grooved petioles up to 10 cm long; alternately arranged; broad to ovate-oblong in shape with an obtuse to subacute tip and a truncate to cordate base. Branches densely covered with soft, white or buff-coloured tomentum.

- *Flowers:* Aug–Nov; fragrant white flower heads each 5 mm across borne profusely on large, much-branched panicles; panicles erect near top of tree but often drooping lower down.
- *Fruit:* ripens Feb; small, hard, dry, single-seeded, hairy fruit.

Distribution & Habitat

- From North Cape south to Kaikoura and Greymouth in forest, along forest margins and in scrub.
- Sea level to 750 m.

▼ Upper surface of a broad leaf.

◄ Tree in full flower showing the leaf upper surfaces, Sept.

32

Poroporo
Solanum aviculare and *S. laciniatum*

Appearance

- Openly branching shrubs or small trees. *S. aviculare* has green to purplish stems. *S. laciniatum* always has purplish stems.
- *Height:* up to 3 m.
- *Bark:* greenish; smooth.

Foliage, Flowers & Fruit

- *Foliage:* soft, membraneous leaves are dark green above with prominent midvein, pale below; 15–30 (up to 40) cm long on petioles extending down at their bases, fused to branchlet; linear-lanceolate or lanceolate in shape, either entire or irregularly pinnatifid.
- *Flowers:* most of year; in 1–3, several or many-flowered cymes. *S. aviculare* lavender or white, up to 3.5 cm across. *S. laciniatum* dark blue-purple, up to 5 cm across.
- *Fruit:* ripens Apr; red-orange, ovoid berries.

Distribution & Habitat

- *S. aviculare* on Kermadec and Poor Knights Is., from Auckland south to Banks Peninsula in east and Karamea in west. *S. laciniatum* from Auckland south to Dunedin. Both in scrub and along coastal and lowland forest margins.

- Sea level to 300 m.

▲ LEFT: Leaves of *S. laciniatum*, upper sides.

▲ RIGHT: Flowers of *S. laciniatum*, Oct. (x1)

▶ Berries of *S. aviculare*, Apr. (x0.6)

◀ A shrub of *S. laciniatum* in flower, Dec.

33

Ngaio
Myoporum laetum

Appearance

- Tree with stout, spreading branches; dome-shaped and low-growing in exposed places.
- *Height:* up to 10 m.
- *Trunk:* up to 30 cm through.
- *Bark:* greyish-brown; rough, wrinkled, corky.

Foliage, Flowers & Fruit

- *Foliage:* fleshy leaves are bright green and gland-dotted above, paler and duller below with prominent midvein; 4–10 cm long, 1–3 cm wide on flattened petioles up to 3 cm long; alternately arranged; lanceolate to oblong-lanceolate in shape, with crenulate-serrulate margins along upper halves, sinuate in lower halves or sinuate only. Tips of branchlets and leaf buds sticky.
- *Flowers:* Dec; bisexual; white flowers with purple-spotted corolla lobes arise in clusters of 2–6 on leaf

▼ A dome-shaped ngaio.

axils on upper parts of branchlets, each 1–1.5 cm across on peduncles up to 15 mm long.

- *Fruit:* ripens March; pale to dark purple, ovoid drupes up to 9 mm long.

Distribution & Habitat

- From Three Kings Is., throughout North Is. and in South Is. south to Otago, and on the Chatham Is., along coastal or lowland forest margins.
- Sea level to 150 m.

▼ Branchlets with flowers and the undersides of mature leaves, Dec. (x0.6)

▼ Foliage spray showing gland-dotted leaves on their flattened petioles. (x0.45)

▶ Branchlets with ripening drupes, Mar. (x0.5)

34

Puriri
Vitex lucens

Appearance

- Massive tree with stout, spreading branches with four-angled branchlets.
- *Height:* up to 20 m.
- *Trunk:* up to 1.5 m through.
- *Bark:* grey–light brown; smooth; peeling when older.

Foliage, Flowers & Fruit

- *Foliage:* rather leathery, undulate leaves are glossy dark green above with distinct venation, paler below with clear venation and domatia (pits); compound leaf on petioles 3.5–12.5 cm long, with 3–5 leaflets per leaf; upper three

5–12.5 cm long, 3–5 cm wide; oppositely aranged; elliptic-oblong to obovate in shape, with acute to acuminate tips and entire margins.

- *Flowers:* most of year; pinkish-red flowers 2.5–3.5 cm in diameter borne in great abundance on 4–15 flowered axillary cymes.
- *Fruit:* most of year; bright red, ovoid drupes about 2 cm across.

Distribution & Habitat
- North Cape to Coromandel and Bay of Plenty in the east and Cape Egmont in the west, in coastal and lowland forests.
- Sea level to 200 m.

▼ Clusters of flowers at the tip of a branchlet, Sept.

▼ The paler lower surface of the compound leaf.

◀ Ripening drupes, Feb. (x0.5)

35 Mangrove / Manawa
Avicennia marina var. *resinifera*

Appearance

- Small tree or shrub growing in tidal waters; stout, spreading branches, lower branches nearly horizontal over water; broad, flat, leafy crown. Widespread roots send up numerous erect breathing roots resembling asparagus shoots, visible at low tide.
- *Height:* 30–50 cm at Kawhia and Ohiwa; to 5 m around Whangarei; to 15 m in the far north.
- *Trunk:* up to 25 cm through.
- *Bark:* grey; furrowed and gnarled.

Foliage, Flowers & Fruit

- *Foliage:* thick, leathery leaves are mid green above, clad in white or buff-coloured tomentum below; 5–10 cm long, 2–4 cm wide, on narrow, winged petioles up to 1 cm long; oppositely arranged; elliptic-oblong to ovate in shape, with more or less pointed tips. Branchlets hairy.
- *Flowers:* Feb–Apr; in small 4–8-flowered clusters on erect, 4-angled pubescent peduncles up to 2 cm long. Each creamy flower 6–7 mm across.
- *Fruit:* ripens following Jan; flattened, ovoid, pale yellow capsule about 2 cm across containing 4 ovules; floats on water until deposited by tide.

Distribution & Habitat

- From North Cape south to Kawhia Harbour in west and Ohiwa Harbour in east in tidal waters around estuaries and inlets.

A flower bud and flower, Apr. (x5)

Spray of leaves showing fruit capsules, Dec. (x0.25)

Manawa tree at low tide, showing aerial roots coming up through the mud.

36

Ti kouka / Cabbage tree
Cordyline australis

Appearance

- Young tree has a slender, unbranched stem with tufted leaves at top and often leaves covering upper half; older tree has massive caudex or trunk which branches in the upper half, with tufted leaves towards end of branches.

- *Height:* from 12–20 m.
- *Trunk:* tall, straight, up to 1.5 m through when older.
- *Bark:* grey; very thick, corky, rough.

Foliage, Flowers & Fruit

- *Foliage:* long, narrow, thick leaves are shiny mid-green above and below with midrib indistinct; 30–100 cm long, 3–6 cm wide; may droop slightly at tips and bend down from bases when old; grow in tufts.
- *Flowers:* Oct; large panicles 60–150 cm long by 30–60 cm wide bear strongly scented white or creamy-white flowers.

- *Fruit:* ripens Feb; bluish-white, ovoid berries to 5 mm across.

Distribution & Habitat

- North, South and Stewart Is., along forest margins, in clearings and around swamps.
- Sea level to 600 m.

▼ The thick, corky, rough bark.

▼ Close view of flowers on a panicle, Dec. (x2)

◀ A very old ti kouka in full flower, Nov.

37

Ti ngahere / Ti parae / Forest cabbage tree
Cordyline banskii

Appearance

- Small tree usually with several stems or branches arising near ground which bear tufted leaves at their tops.
- *Height:* up to 4 m.
- *Trunk:* up to 15–20 cm through.
- *Bark:* grey-brown; rough, furrowed.

Foliage, Flowers & Fruit

- *Foliage:* long, narrow leaves are mid-green above and below; 1–2 m long, 4–8 cm wide, broadest at middle, drooping from there; narrow basally into channelled petiole $\frac{1}{4}$–$\frac{1}{5}$th length of leaf.
- *Flowers:* Oct–Nov; openly branched panicles 1–2 m long

▼ Ti ngahere with flower panicles visible, Nov.

bearing white or creamy flowers, more distantly spaced than in *C. australis*.

- *Fruit:* ripens Feb–Mar; white or bluish, ovoid berry, 4–5 mm across.

Distribution & Habitat

- From North Cape south to about Westport along forest margins or rocky places in wet regions.
- Sea level to 1050 m.

▼ Section of flower panicle, Nov.

▼ Spray showing berries, Mar.

38 Toii / Broad-leaved or mountain cabbage tree
Cordyline indivisa

Appearance
- Massive caudex or trunk that seldom branches, with tuft of sword-shaped leaves at top.
- *Height:* 8 m.
- *Trunk:* up to 20–25 cm through.
- *Bark:* brown; rough, thick, flaky but smooth, blistered after flakes fall.

Foliage, Flowers & Fruit
- *Foliage:* leaves are mid-green above and below, with a conspicuous broad midrib, often reddish; 1–2 m long, 10–15 cm wide; leaves unequal, nerves angled to midrib, often reddish; become narrow near expanded bases to short petioles; droop when old forming curtain of dead leaves around base.

- *Flowers:* Dec; large, tightly compact, many-branched, drooping panicles 60 cm–1.6 m long, 30 cm wide, arise from trunk below tufts of leaves. Flowers about 1 cm across, densely packed, whitish-cream to reddish, purplish-brown or greenish-white.
- *Fruit:* ripens Feb–Mar after 12 months; bluish-black berries about 6 mm across; contain many black seeds.

Distribution & Habitat
- From Hunua Ranges south to Fiordland in regions with wet climate; in open parts of forests where plenty of light.
- 450–1350 m.

▼ A flower panicle hanging below the leafy crown, Dec.

▼ A taller toii, with its curtain of dead leaves below the crown.

◄ Toii showing the sword-shaped leaves with their coloured midrib.

39 Nikau
Rhopalostylis sapida

Appearance
- Straight trunk topped with tufted leaves. World's most southern naturally growing palm tree.
- *Height:* up to 10 m or more.
- *Trunk:* up to 25 cm through.
- *Bark:* greyish when mature; ringed with closely spaced leaf scars and when young is green between these.

Foliage, Flowers & Fruit
- *Foliage:* feather-like leaves are dark green above and below; up to 3 m long, 2 m wide with leaflets up to 1 m; large, swollen, light-green sheaths (spathes) at base of leaves.
- *Flowers:* Dec–Feb; inflorescences (much-branched spokes up to 30 cm long) develop within 2 stout spathes arising above leaf scar

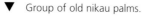

▼ Group of old nikau palms.

below oldest leaf, up to 30 cm long, 15 cm across, falling away when inflorescence starts to expand; bears pink flowers, soon fading to white; male and female flowers arranged in threes.

- *Fruit:* ripens Jan–Feb after 2 years; spikes of brilliant red, hard fruit 10 mm long, 7 mm wide, containing single, large, hard seed.

Distribution & Habitat

- Throughout North Is. in lowland forests, in South Is. south to Banks Peninsula in east and Greymouth in west; also on Chatham Is.
- Sea level to 100 m.

▼ An inflorescence of the present season on top, with inflorescences of the previous season below now bearing fruits, Feb.

▼ A small female flower bud between two male flower buds, and an open male flower, Dec. (x3)

◄ A flower spike in bud with flowers starting to open, and a fruiting spike from the previous year now fully ripe, Feb.

40

Mamaku / Black tree fern
Cyathea medullaris

Appearance

- Tallest of our tree ferns, with a great spreading crown of 20–30 curving fronds and long black trunk.
- *Height:* up to 20 m.
- *Trunk:* up to 30 cm through; black. Trunks of older ferns may be buttressed at base with matted aerial roots. As tree ages, trunk develops distinct hexagonal patterns (leaf scars).

Foliage & Sori

- *Foliage:* leaflets mid-green above, paler below; crown of mature fern may spread over an area 14 m across, with each lamina (thin, flat portion of leaf) up to 6 m long by 2 m wide, with stipe (petioles) up to 1 m long and 9 cm through, densely clothed at its base with long brown scales. Rachides (upper portions of stem) are clothed with brownish scales.
- *Sori:* smooth, round, brown clusters of sporangia form on lower surfaces of pinnules (smallest leaflets), away from the pinnule margin; each sporangium produces about 64 spores.

Distribution & Habitat

- From Three Kings Is. south through the North, South and Stewart Is. and the Chatham Is., in forest and forest margins.
- Sea level to 600 m.

▲ Sori on the pinnules. (x3)

▶ Top: Lower surface of a portion of a rachis.

▶ Bottom: Upper surface of a portion of a rachis showing the clothing of brownish scales.

41

Ponga / Silver fern
Cyathea dealbata

Appearance

- Easily recognised by silver undersides of the lamina and bases of the stipes; the fern of our silver fern emblem. Tall, straight trunk with crown of rather horizontally spreading fronds.
- *Height:* up to 10 m.
- *Trunk:* up to 45 cm through; dark brown. Some withered and dead leaves persist around the base. Some older ferns leave a pattern of projecting stipe bases on the upper half of trunk as they fall off.

Foliage & Sori

- *Foliage:* leaflets deep green to yellow above and silvery or yellowish-white below; each frond 2–4 m long by 60 cm–1.2 m wide; upper surfaces of rachis and secondary rachides covered when young with yellowish-brown hairs but become smooth as frond ages. Bases of the stipes clothed with glossy, dark brown scales.
- *Sori:* smooth, round, brown clusters of sporangia form on lower surfaces of pinnules (smallest leaflets).

▼ A young silver fern.

Distribution & Habitat

- Common throughout North, South and Chatham Is. in forest and sometimes in scrub.
- Sea level to 600 m.

RIGHT: Underside of a portion of
▼ frond showing the hairy rachis and dense waxy bloom.

LEFT: Sori on the undersides of the
▼ pinnules.

◄ Upper surface of portion of a frond.

42

Wheki
Dicksonia squarrosa

Appearance

- Medium-sized tree fern with a slender trunk, slender stipes and fronds that spread more or less horizontally. Easily recognised by the brown colour of the persistent dead fronds.
- *Height:* up to 10 m.
- *Trunk:* up to 45 cm through; dark brown. Bases of the stipes persist down the trunk after leaves have broken away.

Foliage & Sori

- *Foliage:* 9 to more than 20 stiff fronds, harsh to the touch, are dark green above and pale yellow-green below with distinct venation on pinnae; 1.2–1.5 m long, 60–75 cm wide; clothed with long, dark brown, deciduous hairs up to 4 cm long; rachis is rough and hairy when young but smoother and hairless with age. No scales on stipes and rachis.

- *Sori:* smooth, globular clusters of sporangia form on lower surfaces of pinnules (smallest leaflets) on margins, almost completely covering them. Wheki can also multiply by adventitious roots or runners; runners spread out from parent and produce buds that grow into new ferns.

Distribution & Habitat

- Characteristically grow in groves or colonies; abundant in forest throughout the North, South, Stewart and Chatham Is.
- Sea level to 760 m.

▼ Top section of a frond, upper surface.

▼ Sori almost completely covering the pinnules.

Glossary

acuminate: tapering to a fine point

acute: sharply pointed

alternate: arising singly along an axis

anther: the pollen-bearing part of a stamen

apex: tip of a leaf or other organ

appressed: closely and flatly pressed against a surface

aril: accessory seed covering, usually pulpy

ascending: growing upwards, usually at a narrow angle from the vertical

axil: the upper angle between two dissimilar parts

axillary: placed in the axil of a leaf

berry: a fleshy fruit containing a number of seeds but not a 'stone'

bloom: a white powdery cladding

calyx: the outer, usually greenish-coloured whorl of parts in a flower

capsule: a dry fruit that splits open to release its seeds

carpel: the female unit of a flower consisting of the ovary, style and stigma

catkin: a spike-like inflorescence with unisexual flowers

compound: formed of several similar parts

compressed: flattened

cone: the fruiting parts of a conifer

cordate: heart-shaped with the notch at the base

crenate: with shallow, rounded teeth

cuneate: wedge-shaped

cyme: an inflorescence, usually symmetrical, with the oldest flowers innermost (adj. cymous)

deciduous: losing its leaves in the autumn

dentate: with sharp teeth at right angles to the margin

domatia: small pits on the lower surface of a leaf or between the mid and lateral veins

drupe: a fruit with a 'stone' or seed surrounded by a fleshy layer

fascicles: tight clusters

frond: a leaf, especially of ferns

fruit: the ripened ovary containing the seeds

hair: an elongated cell growing from the epidermis

imparipinnate: a pinnate leaf with a single terminal pinna

inflorescence: a general term for the flowering parts

keel: a sharp central ridge

lamina: a thin, flat portion, especially of a leaf

lanceolate: lance-shaped

leaflet: one element of a compound leaf

linear: very narrow with parallel margins

opposite: (of leaves) with a pair arising at the same level on opposite sides of the stem

ovate: (of leaves) egg-shaped, and attached by the broader end

ovoid: egg-shaped

ovule: the young seed within the ovary

panicle: branched, indeterminate inflorescence

pedicel: the stalk of an individual flower

peduncle: a stalk bearing one or many flowers

perianth: the sepals and petals of a flower taken together

petiole: the stalk of a leaf

phylloclade: a flattened stem which functions as a leaf

pinnate: compound with the parts arranged on either side of the axis

pinnule: smallest division of a pinnate leaf, as in a fern

raceme: an unbranched indeterminate inflorescence

rachis (rhachis): the axis of an inflorescence or of a compound leaf

receptacle: the expanded apical portion of the stalk on which the flower is borne

scale: a minute, leaf-like structure, usually dry and membraneous

serrate: sharply toothed

serrulate: with very small, sharp teeth

sessile: without any stalk

sinuate: wavy-edged, with distinct inward and outward bends along the edge

sorus: a cluster of sporangia as occurs in ferns (pl. sori)

spike: an unbranched, indeterminate, elongate inflorescence with sessile flowers

sporangium: a sac or similar structure containing spores (pl. sporangia)

stamen: the male organ of a flower

stipe: that part of a fern leaf corresponding to the petiole

stoma: a pore in the leaf epidermis through which gases pass (pl. stomata)

tepal: an individual member of the perianth of a flower

tomentum: a dense covering of more or less matted, appressed, soft hairs (adj. tomentose)

truncate: with the apex appearing as cut squarely across

umbel: a more or less umbrella-shaped inflorescence with its pedicels arising from a common centre

vein: a strand of conducting and usually strengthening tissue in a leaf

venation: the arrangement of the veins in a leaf

whorl: an arrangement of three or more parts at the same level around an axis

Index of common names

Index of scientific names